FAMILY TIME

Family Time

The Handbook

LINDSAY AND MARK MELLUISH

KINGSWAY PUBLICATIONS
EASTBOURNE

1

A Vision for the Family

What has happened to parenting?

It used to be that parenting skills were passed down, mistakes were learned from and new discoveries were shared. This does not happen so much any more, because of the ways in which our communities have changed.

The reality is that there is much we can learn about parenting.

Leading the family

More than ever, our families need us to lead them today. In the past families were able – far more than they are now – to rely on role models in the community to teach children the principles that govern life. We cannot expect that in our present culture, so our families need *us*, Mum and Dad, to lead them.

Chart the course before the ship sets sail

It is very easy to head out into family life without knowing which way we are going. But how much better to have a destination in mind and to feel secure in where we are heading.

It is all about the destination of our family.

Family values

That end destination will shape the values we have in our family, and those values will shape the way in which we work as a family in the here and now. They will give our family its individual feel – its DNA.

The destination and resulting values will prevent us as a family from being blown off course and away from our end objective.

As we set in place values for our family, however old our children may be, if they know and share those values, those values will always remain. The family values of love, kindness, gentleness, humility, patience, respect and forgiveness need never change.

There is a lovely story in the Bible (in Luke 15) of a son who went off, probably in his teenage years, and spent his father's inheritance and got into all sorts of trouble. But there was something inside him that still wanted home. When he was in trouble, it was home that he went to, because he knew that he would find the value of forgiveness there. He knew that his father would take him back. If he had not known that value, he may not have returned.

So ask yourself: what is the DNA of my family? It is all about the feel of your family and the way in which your family is made up: the atmosphere at home, the relationships between various family members, the depth and maturity of those relationships, the quality of your family time together, how meals operate, how the family communicates (the things you say to each other, what you talk about), and whether you are a family that is outward-looking and seeking in any way to make a difference in society.

Then ask yourself: what is my vision or dream of family life? What is the picture I have of family life as I would wish it to be? What do I most want for my children?

Dream dreams for your family

Take a few moments to think about your hopes and dreams for your family. Write down your top three dreams for your children's lives:

1.

2.

3.

How long does it take for dreams to come true? Rarely do our dreams come true overnight. It helps to have the long term in mind.

Nothing worth having comes easily.

We have all had times when we have, in desperation, gone for the quick option in order to solve an immediate crisis in dealing with our children. We may have resorted to one of the following:

- The *authoritarian* option – 'Do as I say, not as I do.'
- The *permissive* option – 'I'm worn out with it all, so I'll ignore what they're doing and hope they soon grow out of it.'

- The *bribery* option – 'Clean your room, and I'll treat you to an ice cream.'
- The *emotional blackmail* option – 'I won't love you if you do that.'
- The *punishment-driven* option – 'If you don't stop that I'll...' (In other words, we seek control through threat of punishment rather than using punishment as a corrective measure.)

Parenting is all about relationship, about passing on values and understanding to the next generation. It takes time.

In his book *The Seven Habits of Highly Effective Families*, Steven Covey writes about the bamboo tree:

> After the seed for this amazing tree is planted you see nothing, absolutely nothing, for four years except for a tiny shoot coming out of a bulb. During those four years all the growth is underneath in a massive fibrous root structure that spreads deep and wide in the earth. But then in the fifth year the tree grows to eighty feet![1]

Family life is often like that. We do not always see the growth until the very end. The results may not show until adult life. We have the opportunity to influence and shape the future of our children's lives, and that process begins at birth.

The heart

In this course we want to encourage you to reach your children's hearts. We do not want to focus on outward behaviour, but rather to start from inside and work out.

**It is from our hearts that we are motivated
to do things in life.**

If we can reach our children's hearts with healthy values, then ultimately we will see those same values worked out in their lives. Our aim is for any outward change in behaviour to be the result of an inner change of heart.

The Bible says in Proverbs 4:23, 'Above all else, guard your heart, for it is the wellspring of life.' The way our children behave – the things they say and do – reflects their hearts. If we are to reach our children's hearts, then our own hearts have to be reached as well. What we do is also an expression of what is going on inside.

Why use the Bible?

It comes down to a question of relatives or absolutes. Either we have a firm foundation from which to base decisions (an absolute), or we have a life based on moving ground.

We are given children as a gift from God, and into their lives we can build structures that will prepare them for life. The best teaching and value system we can give our children is the value system that God has given us in the Bible.

The Bible touches every area of life in some way or other, either specifically or more generally. If we use it to guide and enlighten us, it will almost certainly enhance our parenting.

Some of the guidelines for life we find in the Bible are very specific, such as 'Do not steal' and 'Do not lie', and these are values that most people would want to place in their children's hearts.

Some things are less specific, but can help us with our parenting nonetheless. Principles such as 'Love your neighbour as yourself' leave us to work out the implications for ourselves.

Our example

Children may not be very good at listening to their elders, but they nearly always seem to find ways of imitating them.

Our influence is crucial. Statistics tell us that patterns of behaviour are often repeated in families.

During the first few years of our children's lives, we are the heroes. Children want to be like their parents. Nothing matters more to them than what we think. As parents we are given the joy and responsibility of being role models for our children. *We reproduce who we are, not what we say!* We must try to be the kind of people we want our children to be.

It is unreasonable to expect a child to listen to your advice and ignore your example.

It is all about the heart. When we train the heart of a child we train the whole child.

Taking it further

1. Think about the hopes and dreams that you have for your family at this stage.
2. Try providing the reason *why* when you ask your child to do something (if you do not do this already), and note the response.
3. Try to consider the circumstances before making parenting decisions this week. See how it helps you in your parenting.

4. In the light of what you have just heard, review the example that you set to your children now, or, if your children are very young (or they have not arrived yet), think about the example you hope to set in the future.
5. Read Chapter 1 of *Family Time*.

Recommended reading for this session

Lindsay and Mark Melluish, *Family Time*, Kingsway Publications, 2002

2

Love and Marriage

The family is the primary social unit of our society, indeed of every society, and it is one worth protecting and keeping. For relationships to grow, the people involved in them need to spend time together. Without time together, families become fragmented.

Perhaps one of the most important areas to focus on in terms of strengthening our family units is that of the relationship between Mum and Dad.

Mum and Dad's relationship

Where possible, the primary relationship in a family is that between Mum and Dad. The way you treat each other will be reflected in the way other members treat each other.

Theodore Hesberg said, 'The most important thing a father can do for his children is to love their mother.'

Wise words from God's word

It says in Genesis 2 that God created man and then decided:

- 'It is not good for the man to be alone' (verse 18).
- 'For this reason a man will leave his father and mother and be united to his wife, and they will become one flesh' (verse 24).

So we see that God's purpose for marriage and in creating woman was to provide a companion for man – someone with whom he could share his life. We were meant to be together. God looked upon the coming together of the man and woman as 'very good'. A man and woman who are married to one another are complete. When children arrive, their family increases in size, but the children do not make them any more of a family.

How does all this affect us now?

Our relationship with our partner is the most important relationship in the family. The quality of all the relationships in the family, and also the security of our children, will depend on the quality of Mum and Dad's relationship.

Nothing we can buy or do for our children is more important than showing them that Mum and Dad love and value one another and that together we lead the family.

What if you are parenting on your own?

Life can be and often is very hard for those who are bringing up children without the support of a partner. If you are parenting on your own:

- Your relationship with God, if you have one, makes a difference as you rely on him to help you raise the family, and this is a good and positive means of outward focus. It will also be a source of support and strength in your parenting, because God is someone who loves to listen and care.

- Let your children know how important your relationship with God is. Bring them to worship regularly and mix with other families. Get support from your church family. Let the children draw security from seeing you spend time with God, and allow the strength you draw from him to be a source of stability in your relationships both inside and outside the family.

Families whose lives revolve around the children

To live our lives completely centred around the children may bring problems for various reasons:

- If we allow our children always to be our priority, *our focus shifts away from our partner* and we no longer fulfil our role as husband or wife. Instead we tend to hide behind the role of Mum or Dad, where we can feel less exposed and accountable.
- If we are parenting on our own, having our child as the central focus of our life can lead to that child, as he or she gets older, taking the place of a husband or wife. In this way *the child becomes an equal and a friend to Mum or Dad* – a relationship that is difficult for a child to cope with.
- To build our lives around the life of a child can give him *the feeling that he is self-reliant* – 'I can manage on my own and I don't need anyone else.' We are not saying, of course, that a child should not be encouraged to do things for himself, but to foster a sense of not needing other people might put him at a disadvantage in the long term. Our children will benefit so much from learning that other people matter, regardless of whether they will always gain personally from maintaining a relationship with them.
- If our lives revolve solely around the children we may give them

more freedom than they can cope with – and if this happens before they have acquired the self-control to manage such freedom, they will quite likely come a cropper.

- *We may find it difficult to set boundaries for our children*, and may find ourselves having to adapt the boundaries rather than face addressing the behaviour of our child.

If a child learns that he is at the centre of the family, he may tend to be self-centred and have difficulty in making relationships both inside and outside the family unit. He will tend to be a taker and not a giver. On the other hand, a child who sees his place in the family more as a member of a team will be confident and secure about where he fits in. He will therefore make relationships naturally and comfortably, giving as well as receiving, and growing up knowing the importance of investing in family relationships and caring for others.

How can we make Mum and Dad's relationship a priority?

- Remember, *life does not stop when you have children.*
- When you arrive home, *make a point of saying 'hello' to your husband or wife.* If you are parenting on your own, you could ask your family and friends, and particularly your own parents, to make a point of greeting you first when they arrive before making a fuss of the children. Explain to them that you want the children to see you valuing other close relationships as well as your relationship with them.
- Try to *take time to talk to your husband or wife every day without interruptions* – when the children are around to see, not after they are in bed.
- *Guard your privacy* by asking the children to knock on your bedroom door before they come in.
- *If you are parenting on your own and it is your habit to pray, try doing it when the children are awake,* and let them know that this is something that is helpful for you. Once they are used

to it and understand it, they may well draw security from this and look forward to your time spent with God. If this does not work for you, however, try to find another way of making sure the focus is not always on the children.

- *Do something together* as husband and wife, say, once a week. If you are parenting on your own, do the same, but with a good friend or family member. Be sure to get out and do something for yourself and with someone other than your children. Keep up your contacts outside the family.
- *Use your home to serve other people.*

How can I learn to say, 'I love you'?

In marriage and family life love is not always the easiest thing in the world! There are times when we have to *choose* to love.

Wise words from God's word

'And over all these virtues put on love...' (Colossians 3:14).

If love were just a feeling, then we would not be able to 'put it on'. In marriage and family relationships, we choose to love and this choice will lead to action.

Accounts for love

Each of us has a 'love bank'. It is a bank with many different accounts in it. In fact, it has an account for each and every person we know. Each person makes either a deposit or a withdrawal every time we interact with them. Pleasurable interactions result in deposits and painful interactions result in withdrawals.

We affect each other emotionally with almost every encounter.

The love languages

Another similar idea is that each of us has a love tank which is waiting to be filled with love. Why is it that so often our love tanks are on empty? Why do we sometimes not truly feel loved? One answer is that people are different, and different people speak different love languages (see recommended reading).

If we are to be effective communicators of love, we must be willing to learn our partner's primary love language (or the way they most readily give and receive love). Below are the five love languages:

1. Words of affirmation
2. Quality time
3. Gifts
4. Acts of service
5. Physical touch

Our children and their love languages

We parents love our children, and equally we want our children to feel that they are loved. If you can discover your child's primary love language, you will be at a distinct advantage in loving your child in a way that makes him *feel* loved as well as just knowing that you love him. Pour on all five love languages, then watch carefully to see which is your child's particular language.

- If your child is always making and wrapping presents for you and responds very positively when given a gift, *receiving gifts* may be his primary love language. He gives because he likes to receive. If so, gifts do not have to be expensive or cost anything at all. The fact that they are given will be enough to fill the tank.
- If your child runs to you and jumps on your lap when you arrive and strokes your hair and wants to be touched, his primary love language may be *physical touch*. If so, give him plenty of hugs and kisses, as many as he can take.
- If your child always comes and shows you things he has written or drawn, and looks for praise or responds very positively when his behaviour is praised, then *words of affirmation* may be his primary love language. If so, give him lots of encouragement. Praise his successes rather than highlighting his failures – and this, of course, goes for all children anyway.
- All children need quality time, some more than others. What you can do is to enter into their interests, watch them playing sport, listen to them practising the piano, give them the time they are looking for. If you do this when they are young, the chances are that they will allow you to spend time with them in their adolescent years and beyond.
- If your child is often very grateful for the things you do for him and often offering to help you, his primary love language may be *acts of service*. Helping him to mend his bicycle or a toy will mean a lot to him and help to fill his tank.

How can we discover our *own* primary love language? Ask yourself these questions:

- What makes me feel most loved by my partner? What do I desire above all else?
- What does my partner do or say that hurts me? (If criticism springs to mind, maybe your love language is words of affirmation.)
- What have I most requested of my partner? The thing you most

request is probably the thing that would most make you feel loved.

● How do I most express love to my partner? Often we express love in the way we would like it expressed to us.

Take time now to do the 'love languages exercise' below, using it to work out your primary love language and then to work out the order of the other four. Try to work out the order for your partner and for your children as well.

Enjoy the difference it makes to your family life as you seek to put love into action!

Love languages exercise

Remember that the five love languages are:

1. Words of affirmation
2. Quality time
3. Gifts
4. Acts of service
5. Physical touch

Spend time now, by yourself, deciding on the love languages of your partner in priority order – i.e. the language that you think he or she most speaks and responds to (1) down to the one he or she speaks/responds to least (5). Then do the same for yourself.

My partner's love languages are:	*My love languages are:*
1	1
2	2
3	3
4	4
5	5

When you have completed your lists, compare them with those your spouse has drawn up. Later on, do the same exercise for your children's love languages.

My children's love languages are:

1	1	1	1
2	2	2	2
3	3	3	3
4	4	4	4
5	5	5	5

Taking it further

1. Consider this question: does your family revolve chiefly around your children, or, on the other hand, are the needs of each member of the family considered to be equally important?
2. This week, when you come home in the evening, try spending five minutes talking with your husband or wife before taking time with the children. See how your children respond.
3. Read Chapter 2 of *Family Time*.

Recommended reading for this session

Gary Chapman, *The Five Love Languages*, Northfield Publishing, 1995

John and Anne Coles, *Making More of Marriage*, New Wine International, 2000

Willard F. Harley, *His Needs, Her Needs*, Fleming H Revell Co., 1995

Nicky and Sila Lee, *The Marriage Book*, HTB Publications London, 2000

Rob Parsons, *Loving Against the Odds*, Hodder & Stoughton, 1998

3

When They Are Young

We hope to reach our children's hearts so that we might enable them ultimately to live a life which brings fulfilment and contentment. It is helpful if:

- our relationships with them are strong;
- channels of communication are always open;
- our children know we love them.

The time when we, as parents, have most influence and opportunity to shape and guide our children's lives is when they are very young – and it is a relatively short period, perhaps between ten and twelve years. The first thing that helps us towards our hopes and dreams is being present with our family. Children need our time today, and it is not just quality time they need, but quantity time.

Presence is spelt T-I-M-E.

A key to communicating with children is to put in a lot of quantity time so that the quality time can happen.

If we are to build an open, honest, trusting relationship with our children in which they are able to come to us with confidence whatever the problem and whatever their age, we will need to invest time, both quality and quantity.

25

The best thing parents can spend on children is time, not money.

A report that recently came out from Harvard University said that the single most common factor producing anger, rage and hostility in children was the perceived inaccessibility of one or both of their parents. Our presence matters.

Take a few moments now to discuss the chart below with your partner or neighbour, and use it to review the time you spend with your children.

1. Write down in the first column the amount of time per session that you are available to your children this week.
2. Write down in the second column the amount of time you are able to give them your full attention.

	Weekday Time Available	Weekday Full Attention	Saturday Time Available	Saturday Full Attention	Sunday Time Available	Sunday Full Attention
Morning						
Early Afternoon						
Late Afternoon						
Evening						
Total this week:						

What can we do to encourage communication with our children?

So often parents are telling their children what to do while the children are trying to tell their parents their dreams and wishes.

Sometimes we make the mistake of thinking that communication is the ability to express ourselves. So we talk *to* our children rather than talking *with* them. Our object in communication with our children must surely be to understand them. How can we learn to listen?

Practical tips

- Physically get down to the level of your child. Perhaps kneel or sit when he is talking.
- Look him in the eye. Show him that he has your full attention.
- Do not try to do two things at once. Listen only to your child.
- Reassure him that he has your attention by touching him on the face or arm.
- Wait for him to finish what he is saying! It may take a while, but it is worth it.

What will be the end result? To communicate with your children is to invest long-term in their characters. The more you talk with your children, helping them to understand themselves, their temptations, doubts, fears and anxieties, the more you will prepare them for life in the world. You will also teach them that their thoughts are of value and that you want to understand them better because they matter so much to you.

Communication at a deeper level will help you to get in touch with the heart of your child and hear his inner feelings.

Three worlds

We all have three worlds:

- Our public world, the part of us that is open for anyone to see.
- Our personal world, which is open to those close to us.
- Our private world, which we open up just every now and then to those we trust.

Children have the same three worlds, and from time to time as parents we are invited into that very private world.

Communication is the art of expressing sensitively what is in your heart, and of hearing completely and understanding what another thinks or feels. *Allow your children into your world too.*

Building relationships

Communication at a deeper level is our aim. Building relationships is the key to that aim. What can we do to build relationships with our children and ensure that they really do feel that we love them?

1. Do things together

As we spend time with our children we find that, very often, good conversation follows. Making time to do things together creates an environment in which we can talk with our children about important things. Our children will probably learn more from talking with Mum and Dad than we will ever realize.

2. Encourage with words

It says in 1 Thessalonians 5:11, 'Encourage one another and build each other up.' The word 'encourage' means 'to instil courage'. In giving our children encouragement we are looking to give them the courage to go further, to enlarge their borders.

Children need to hear words that inspire and encourage them. As parents we have the power to discourage or encourage by what we say to our children.

Speak words of encouragement:

- 'Thank you for taking out the rubbish. That really helps me.'
- 'Well done for getting yourself dressed. You've really learned to do that quickly now.'
- 'You've worked very hard at [learning to play football/getting dressed in the morning/leaving your bedroom tidy/picking up your toys] and it's made a real difference.'

Words like this, which emphasize effort and improvement, are such motivators. We have noticed how often such words genuinely help our children to achieve their potential.

Words do not have to be spoken – they can be written too.

Another important thing to remember is that we need to allow our children the freedom to fail. An encouraging parent looks for effort rather than success. Let's look for improvement and seek to encourage and inspire our children in every way possible.

3. Give plenty of hugs

Studies have shown that many parents only touch their children when it is necessary, such as when they are dressing them, putting them in the car, or taking them up to bed. Yet hugging is a very effective way of making our children feel loved. As parents, we can develop a relationship with our children that is not just verbal but physical too. Children of all ages and both sexes need physical expressions of love.

4. Keep your promises

To build trust and communication we have to be trustworthy. If we can be trustworthy and keep our word, then our children are more likely to grow to be the same.

**Our memories are all too short,
but our children's are not.**

---

5. Tell your children regularly that you love them

Use sign language to get your loving message across – especially fun in a crowded place.

And finally, a word to the dads...

An article in *The Times* (28 January 1999) said, 'Fathers who devote time to their sons – even as little as five minutes a day – are giving them a far greater chance to grow up as confident adults, a parenting research project has found.' It went on, 'Boys who feel that their fathers devote time especially to them and talk about their worries, school work and social lives almost all emerge as motivated and optimistic young men full of confidence and hope.'

Building boys is better than mending men.

Dads play a special part in the family. Often today, dads are away from home for much of the time. Yet our boys need us around as male role models, and for the rough-and-tumble games that boys love to play. And our girls need us to affirm their femininity. Dads have an equally crucial role to play in family life as mums do, and we want to encourage them to play their full part in bringing up the children.

The central message is this: *build relationships with your children while you have the chance.* When our children are young, we – as mums and dads – are largely in control of all they do. God made it this way because our children have been entrusted to us and we, through our love and care, will look after them. As they grow older, however, our control diminishes as they begin to make their own decisions and choices. We hope that in place of that control will come our guiding influence – but this will only be possible if we have laid firm foundations for the relationship between us and our children. We found the following diagram very helpful to illustrate this.[1]

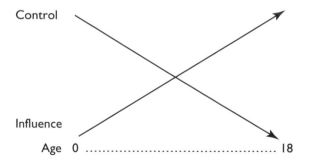

Our influence will only be as great as the effort we have put into making strong relationships. Our aim must be to build a relationship that will stand the test of time. As we spend time with our children now, building a relationship of trust, we are laying the foundations for a life of unity in the family.

Taking it further

1. Begin to work on listening and communicating in the ways this session has suggested, and see how your child responds.
2. Try to be aware this week of how good you are at listening to your partner or to other adults.
3. Look for opportunities to encourage and praise your children.
4. Read Chapter 3 of *Family Time*.

Recommended reading for this session

Gary Chapman and Ross Campbell, *The Five Love Languages for Children*, Northfield Publishing, 1995

Adele Faber and Elaine Maglish, *How to Talk so Kids Will Listen and Listen so Kids Will Talk*, Avon Books, 2002

Rob Parsons, *The Sixty Minute Father*, Hodder & Stoughton, 1995

4

Family Time

The way we treat our children will ultimately have quite an effect on how they turn out. Every child will be subject to certain shaping influences, events and circumstances in the developmental years which prove to be catalysts for making him the person he is.

Wise words from God's word

The Bible tells us that our early childhood experience has lifelong implications for us as individuals. It also sheds light on family life and on how children should be treated and brought up (see, for example, Deuteronomy 6, Ephesians 6 and Colossians 3).

The people our children become are a product of two things:

1. *Life experience.* What is life like for our children? In what environment are they being brought up? Are both parents around and, if so, do they have a harmonious relationship?
2. *How they interact with that experience.* Our children react and respond to their circumstances, and our job as parents is to know where our children need guidance and structure to help them respond appropriately, so that they are not blown hither and thither by every wind which comes in their direction.

The family

When our children are very young, the family is one of the major influences on them. Many aspects of family life have a bearing on who our children become.

1. Family structure
2. Family roles
3. Family conflict
4. Family failure
5. Family history
6. Family values

It is never an indication of failure to see a need to make changes in family life. And it is never too late. Now is the time to be proactive in our families and to change things for the better if we feel the need.

Family patterns

The most important model we have of marriage and parenting, for better or worse, is our own family. Jot down your responses to the following points and talk with your partner or neighbour about how similar or different your experiences were.

In my childhood home . . .
We used to make jokes often / sometimes / rarely.
We used to touch each other frequently / sometimes / hardly ever.
Kisses and cuddles were normal / measured / rare.
When people felt angry they hit out / rowed / sulked / talked.
We would discuss our plans fully / partly / reluctantly.
My business was everybody's / interesting / my own.
We prided ourselves on our concern / interest / independence.
Nakedness was accepted / avoided / frowned upon.
Sex was discussed readily / when necessary / never.
Children were disciplined by my Dad / my Mum / both / neither.

Children said prayers with my Dad / my Mum / both / neither.
We went out together / independently / rarely.
I liked it when my Dad . . .
I liked it when my Mum . . .
I was unhappy when . . .

Today in my immediate family . . .
What my child might say they like best about my family is . . .
What I like best about my family is . . .
I can rely on my family to . . .
Something my parents did that I do not want to happen in my home
is . . .
I expect to be in touch with my relatives daily / weekly / monthly / two
or three times a year / as little as possible.

Family identity

If we have a strong family identity, then peer pressure can be
diminished. If family identity is strong, if our children feel
involved in and proud to belong to their family, they are more
likely to hold to its values and principles. Children who feel unin-
volved in their family and have little sense of belonging are more
likely to look outside the family for a sense of identity and a set of
values.

There is great security in belonging to a group, and where family ties are weak, young people often find that security with friends.

Whether you are a couple parenting together, or a single parent
caring for children on your own, there is a great deal you can do
to work at building this strong sense of family identity.

1. Be a team

Being a team encourages a family to be interdependent.
Interdependence encourages family unity and identity. Teams,
when they work together, can achieve a great deal.

As mums and dads we have a special role here, and we can give
the lead in being a team.

Being a team means supporting and encouraging the team members.

We can be a team by:

- Entertaining together.
- Tidying up together.
- Cleaning the car together.
- Serving together to help others.
- Taking part together in a sponsored project in the community.

2. *Have family time*

'Family time' is time set aside, first for Mum and Dad to talk together, and then for the children to join them so that the whole family can be together and each has a chance to share and listen to everyone else.

To have a time set aside for the family at least once a week, when the purpose is to talk and listen to each other, will help to strengthen your family and let every member know in a tangible way that family is your priority. Perhaps one will have a problem and the others can all help to sort it out. Perhaps one is rejoicing over an achievement and the others can share that gladness.

What is the value of family time?

1. It is a place to bring up something that we, as parents, want to talk to the children about, perhaps something related to our life as a family that we need to change or redress.
2. It is a place for the children to bring up things they want to talk about or question.
3. It is a place to teach something new or to introduce something new into family life.
4. It is a place to talk about an important event that is coming up, to prepare for it together by sharing our excitements, our fears and worries.

5. It is a place to laugh together.
6. It is a place to pray together.

Of course, family time will not be the only time we talk with our children! But children do love having this special slot set aside for them, and often respond well to it.

3. Set family jobs

Children will learn if they are allowed to have a go, and in the safety of the home we can stand by to help and guide them. Below is a list of jobs that your children might do to help around the home.

- Set the table for a meal
- Feed pets
- Make drinks
- Make beds in the morning
- Help with cleaning
- Tidy garden of toys
- Pick up litter in garden
- Make cups of tea or coffee
- Clear up their toys after use
- Put dirty clothes in the wash basket
- Clean windows
- Wash car
- Help with washing up
- Help with ironing
- Help with the gardening
- Cook a meal

Giving our children jobs to do builds a sense of responsibility. Jobs which affect the whole family – such as laying the table – are very good for encouraging a sense of team spirit and a willingness later in life to muck in where help is needed.

Too much responsibility too early could be overwhelming, but too little could leave the children believing that you do not trust them.

4. Make a family quote book

This is a fun way of building that sense of being a team. Write down some of the funnier family quotes. As the children get older, they can write in it too.

5. Take family photos

Photos are a great way of recording family history and giving the family a sense of identity.

How about creating a collage at the end of the year which includes photographs of all the important events – birthdays, Christmas, weddings and so on – that have taken place during that year? You could have one for each year that your children have been alive, hung on the wall at home.

6. Create family traditions

Family traditions are simply another way of saying, 'This is us and this is the way we do things together.'

- Start a tradition of taking each child out for a celebratory meal when they reach the age of eleven.
- Start a tradition of having a special family trip to McDonald's or somewhere similar at the end of the school term.
- Start a tradition of having a family walk in the countryside on Bank Holiday Monday.

7. Be together

There are times when life can be so busy with after-school activities, sports clubs, recorder lessons, piano lessons, football coaching, Cubs, Brownies and the many other things that crop up daily. It is therefore good to be creative in our family activities as well.

Mealtimes can be a great opportunity for being together. Sometimes work commitments make it impossible to have a family meal every day. If that is the case, make Sunday lunch special, or Friday supper – whatever fits into your family rhythm.

Do things together:

- Go on cycle rides.
- Have a family pizza night with a good video.
- Go for walks together.
- Eat meals together as often as possible.
- Sleep in the tent together in the garden.
- Sit in church together.
- Eat ice creams together.
- Do the gardening together.
- Read a book together.

Let the children choose sometimes what they would like the whole family to do together. It does not matter what you do, as long as you all enjoy it and you do it together.

Make family holidays a priority, too. You are investing in family memories.

Ask yourself these questions:

- Are we cultivating a sense of team spirit within our family, or is independence valued more than interdependence?
- Is our family one that our children are glad to belong to?
- Do our children feel involved in our family?

The family is an important factor in determining who our children become. We have an opportunity to invest time and energy now that will reap many rewards later in life.

Taking it further

1. Consider the structure of your family and what effect it might have on your child or children. Are there things that you would like to change and can change?

2. Consider steps you might take to strengthen the identity of your family.

3. Try having family time and see how your children respond.

4. Read Chapter 4 of *Family Time*.

5

Outside Influences

As our children grow older and begin to have freedom to be a bit more independent, outside influences become stronger and they are going to be faced not only with positive ideas and activities but negative ones as well. As parents we can be aware of these influences, and try to equip our children to make decisions based on what is right and good.

By the age of seven, or even earlier, our children are being affected by different opinions on all sorts of subjects. Below are some of the influences our children are under outside the family.

Television

Statistics tell us . . .

- The average father spends three minutes a day in 'quality' conversation with his children.
- The average mother spends five and a half minutes a day in 'quality' conversation.
- The average child spends three hours a day watching television.
- Children under five watch an average of two hours' television each day.

The chances are that many of our children's values and views will be shaped by what they see on television.

Wise words from God's word

The Bible says, 'Whatever is true, whatever is noble, whatever is right, whatever is pure, whatever is lovely, whatever is admirable . . . think about such things' (Philippians 4:8).

There are many good children's films, and some very good children's programmes on television, but we have to be selective and not just assume that because it is on children's television it is helpful or healthy to watch.

You might like to use a video recorder to record programmes that you know your children would enjoy, so that the programme is available when you are ready to watch it.

Computers

Articles have been written about computers being used as 'virtual childminders', and it is essential to remember that not everything about computers is educational and good.

- Use computers, but remember to give equal time to playing with your children and encouraging them to play together. It is play that fosters the development of social, language and thinking skills.
- Keep home computers in the 'public' parts of the house, not hidden away in bedrooms.
- Restrict the time any one child can spend on a computer, and vet the games and programmes used.

School

School life is so influential in the lives of our children that it should be a place where we become involved if we possibly can. This might be through offering classroom help, or by becoming part of a parent committee or governing body.

Let's ensure that we work *with* the teachers who have care of our children, so that we can support them as well as have them support us and our children.

Friends

Encourage your children to choose their friends wisely. We can choose friends for our children when they are very young, and after this we can gently educate them to be wise about their friendships.

Peer pressure starts when they are very young.

Wise words from God's word

We are told in Proverbs 13:20, 'He who walks with the wise grows wise, but a companion of fools suffers harm.' The apostle Paul says in 1 Corinthians 15:33, 'Bad company corrupts good character.'

Other adults

Friends' parents, childminders, teachers of outside activities, church children's group leaders – all of them will influence our children in some way or another. We can encourage those relationships with adults whose values we respect and want to pass on to our children.

Be proactive in looking for other adults who can be 'significant others' for your children.

The extended family also has an important place in family life. Grandparents often have more time than we do to play with and read to the children. Uncles, aunties and cousins are all part of the picture too.

The role of mentoring from one generation to another is a valuable thing in the lives of our children. The benefits of developing such relationships are far-reaching and our children gain much from the wisdom and input these other adults are able to offer.

Taking stock

There are so many influences that might affect our children. Take a few moments to look at the list below, and discuss it with your partner or neighbour. Note down how many hours each week your children spend with this person or doing that activity. Then ask yourself how helpful or unhelpful that person or activity is. Try to be as specific as possible.

Ask yourself the following questions:

- Who has the greatest influence on my children?
- Am I happy about this influence?
- Does anything need changing?
- Who else is helping us to bring up our children?

Our children's relationship with God

Let's not make the mistake of concluding that parenting is nothing more than providing the best possible outside influences. Our children respond to their surroundings, to the influences around them, according to where their hearts are.

Children are not just passive receivers of outside influences. They are active responders.

As our children interact with their childhood experience, their response will be affected by all sorts of things, including the following:

- Whether they have *good relationships within the family*, where opinions and problems can be raised and discussed.
- Whether they are *aware of the values of the family* and to what extent they have taken on those values (see Chapter 6 for more on this).
- Whether they have *good relationships with other trusted adults* to whom they can go and discuss things.
- Whether they have *good friendships with peers* who encourage them to fulfil their potential.
- Whether they have been taught to question and *think things through for themselves*.
- Their *perception of God*.

Part of our task as parents is to help our children to worship and honour God in their lives. Our children's understanding of who God is and their own relationship with him will affect their response to life. How can we encourage our children in their relationship with God?

1. Pray for them

If we pray regularly that our children will develop their own relationship with God, there will always be a channel open between their lives and God.

We can also pray for our children's future partner, and for children yet to be born.

**The greatest prayer we can offer for our
children is that they will know a relationship with
their heavenly Father. Children as young as
three can understand enough to have a
meaningful relationship with him.**

---

2. Pray with them

Even one-year-old children can copy you praying, and very quickly
begin to understand the concept of prayer.

- Pray with them before they go to sleep at night.
- Point out to them answers to prayer.
- Pray with them about world situations.
- Pray about things that trouble them or have hurt them.
- Pray at the start of a long car journey.
- Pray before a meal – at home and in restaurants.

3. Be open with your children about your own faith

Look for ways to remind the children of God's goodness as often
as possible.

- Tell them all that you know about God so that they learn from
  you.
- Talk to them about ways in which God has answered your own
  prayers.
- Share with them how God has met a need for you or someone else.

4. Let them see you reading your Bible and praying

It is important for children to know that you are really living out
what you talk to them about.

5. Encourage them to enjoy the Bible themselves

For the older children, consider buying them a Bible of their own
and some fun Bible teaching notes to help them understand what

they are reading. Working through the notes with them will let them know that you think it is important.

For younger children, a toddler Bible or very simple notes are good. Read them Bible stories and talk to them about how these stories apply to their own lives. In the early years, when children love their parents to read to them each night, try reading a regular story and then a Bible story. This means that they will be getting two stories and learning about God at the same time.

6. *Let them see you worshipping in church*

Encourage your children to listen to children's worship tapes, and learn the songs with them.

7. *Read them books with a Christian message.*

Fill their minds with good things. There are so many good books around, and we can encourage our children to enjoy many of them by reading with them or buying them as little presents.

8. *Worship together as a family*

Use these times as opportunities for strengthening and encouraging your children's own personal relationship with God. Family time is a great chance to do this.

Taking it further

1. Review the list of influences on your children and think about any changes you may want to make.
2. Consider your child's relationship with God. Look at how you might encourage him or her to develop that relationship.
3. Read Chapter 5 of *Family Time*.

Recommended reading for this session

Stormie Omartian, *Power of a Praying Parent*, Kingsway Publications, 1996
Various children's books and Bibles

6

Transmitting Values

We aim to be families who do not just seek to survive, but who have vision. That vision involves a desire to bring up children who are confident, capable, secure, happy, courageous, fun-loving, honest, considerate, diligent – children who will ultimately make a difference in this world.

We hope to bring up children who choose to do what is right rather than wrong. We are looking to train their hearts.

Our aim as parents is to bring up children whose lives are an outward expression of a right heart.

Family values

The answers to questions like the ones below will offer clues about particular family values.

- What is a priority and what is not?
- What causes Mum and Dad to 'go mad', and what goes by without them even commenting?
- Are material possessions important, or do friendships and family relationships have greater value?
- Is keeping the house tidy too important to allow friends home for pizza and Coke, or are people welcome in our home at any time?
- What attitudes do the children grow up with?

49

- Is a relationship with God central to family life, or does life go on from week to week without reference to him?

So what are our values? What values are we passing on to our children? Sometimes values are so in-built that we live them out without being conscious of them. Our values can change, too.

- What values did you grow up with in your family?
- What values do you have now?

Look at the list below and see whether or not you agree with the statements.

- God is number one in our lives. No person or thing is more important. We should make time to worship him and should never speak in a way that is dishonouring to him.
- Family relationships are important, especially the ones between parents and children.
- It is wrong to take another person's life.
- Marriage is a God-given thing and is the right place for sex.
- We should always pay for what we want to own unless we are given it as a gift. Stealing is always wrong.
- Honesty and truth are crucial for the smooth running of society. Lies are wrong, as is the dishonesty of putting someone else in a bad light.
- It is wrong to be jealous of what other people have and think that you should have it as well. People are more important than possessions. Other people matter.
- We should respect the law and honour all those in authority over us. Breaking the law will generally hurt others in the end.

This list is based on the Ten Commandments (see Exodus 20:1–17). If you find that you agree with what it contains, then the chances are that many, if not all, of your family values are based on the Bible.

Discuss these values now with your partner or neighbour, then number them 1–8 in order of priority for you.

It is these family values that we want actively to place in the hearts of our children. We want to give them a framework for life. How can we do this?

The conscience

The heart is very closely linked with the work of the conscience, and in fact the Bible speaks of the conscience and the heart in the same way. It is out of our 'heart' or 'conscience', our understanding of what is right and wrong, that our attitudes and values come.

We have this innate framework, which we are then able to fill from life's experiences and learning. God made us with a conscience, but he left much of it empty. He placed there the framework – his ideas – and then left us to fill it or develop it with the values by which we choose to live our lives. We are able to adapt and shape our own value system. While our children are young, we have the opportunity to place in their hearts, in their conscience, the values we believe are important.

Wise words from God's word

Psalm 119:11 sums it up: 'I have hidden your word in my heart that I might not sin against you.' Just as David, the writer of the psalm, hid God's word in his own heart, so we can 'hide', or place, God's word in our children's hearts.

The value library

The heart, or conscience, is the area which receives and stores values – it is a 'value library'. The Bible says in Deuteronomy 6:6–7, 'These commandments that I give you today are to be upon your hearts. Impress them on your children.' We, the parents, are to fill the 'shelves' in our children's hearts with good values.

Value search system

We place good values into the hearts of our children. From this store, or 'library', of knowledge our children are able to find answers to the dilemmas that life throws at them. For each new situation we meet, a 'search system' comes into play, scanning the shelves of the value library – our conscience – for the corresponding value.

Honesty

Honesty is very powerful in building strong, healthy relationships within the family. Without honesty, it is very difficult to maintain a bridge of trust between family members.

There will be times in every family when honesty takes a back seat, and the question is, how do we deal with it? The two most likely occurrences will be:

- Not telling the truth (or lying)
- Taking things that belong to someone else (or stealing)

How do we handle these when they occur?

Not telling the truth

It is important that you try to get behind the behaviour. Consider these aspects:

- *The age of your child.*
- *The motive behind the lie.* This will help you try to correct it. Is your child wanting attention, trying to escape responsibility, or simply copying someone else?
- *Your child's general level of honesty.* Telling a lie in a moment of weakness is different from habitual lying, and should be dealt with differently.

If your child really will not come clean, he may get away with it this time, but at least your relationship will remain intact. And your child will respect you for not disciplining him when you are not sure what really happened.

Taking things that belong to someone else

There are two aspects to consider before you take any action:

- *The seriousness of the theft.* Taking a packet of crisps from the cupboard without permission is not the same as taking £5 from Mum's purse.
- *The context.* Taking a packet of crisps from the cupboard is not the same as taking a packet of crisps from the newsagents.

**Dishonesty within the family reflects on the child;
dishonesty outside the family reflects
on the family.**

Stealing is not always a tangible thing. You can steal someone's time, or you can steal their reputation through gossiping about them. Gossip is something about which God feels strongly (see

Proverbs 6:19). It is difficult to restore someone's reputation once
it has been damaged. Wise parents will teach their children the
importance of being careful about what we say concerning other
people.

How do we input these family values?

In their very early years, we will be directing our children by using
quite a few negatives. So we find ourselves saying 'No' or 'Don't
touch' several times a day.

From around the age of three, however, it is important to
change the approach from this negative form of training to a
much more positive form of shaping. Now we can begin to input
positively into our children's conscience. This will involve instruction, encouragement and reinforcement. It will constantly involve
us in providing the reason 'why' in answer to many of their questions and as an accompaniment to our instructions.

So how is this change of approach seen in the family? In our
house, when the children wake up in the morning, they stay in
their beds and read quietly until Mum and Dad get up and the day
begins. Our older children know the reason behind this: if they
were to get up and play, the noise would wake those who are still
sleeping and the morning would start badly for everyone. A few
years ago one of our children, then about two and a half, moved
from a cot into a bed. She was too young to understand the reason why she should stay bed in the morning, so we simply said
that she must not get out of bed until we said and that if she did,
she would have to sleep in her cot again. Because she did not want
to lose the privilege of sleeping in a bed, she learned to stay in it!

Training through negative consequences can teach an under-
three to do what an over-three might do because he or she under-
stands the reason why.

In time, our children should begin to do things because they are
the right things to do. The value library begins to act by itself.
They may even start to explain to each other why a certain course

of action is right. Then you can really feel you are getting somewhere!

Encouraging a healthy conscience

It is so important to make that change from negative to more positive training. Otherwise we risk frustrating our children, who will not understand the reasons behind what we are requiring of them, even though they have the capacity to do so.

A healthy conscience is what we are looking to develop in our children. A healthy conscience is marked by the attitude, 'I ought to do this because it is right.'

An unhealthy conscience is marked by the attitude, 'I must do this or else I'll be punished.'

A healthy conscience can more easily develop if:

- Children know that their parents love them unconditionally, rather than believing that their love depends on good behaviour.
- Parents try to respond to bad behaviour by correcting it and moving on rather than looking to make the child feel guilty. (This will protect our children from thinking they have to behave in order to avoid feeling guilty.)
- Parents can seek to input strong values and explain the reason for upholding them.

We want to bring up our children to be confident in themselves about what is or is not the right thing to do in a given situation. We want them to act not through fear of guilt or punishment, but through a sheer desire to do the right thing.

- What values are you placing in your children's hearts?
- How are you placing them?
- Are you aware of living out and encouraging in your children good or biblical values, emphasizing that other people matter?

The Healthy Conscience Test

Try doing this test on yourself to see what sort of conscience you have. Give yourself a score for each statement, according to the scale given below.

Scale
 1 = Never true of me
 3 = Sometimes true of me
 5 = Half yes/half no
 7 = Usually true of me
10 = Always true of me

1. I am uncomfortable in a discussion where my view or opinion is different from that of the other person.
2. I find it hard to say 'no' when someone makes a request of me which would add to an already over-busy schedule.
3. When a friend is distant or preoccupied, I tend to assume it is because of something I have done wrong.
4. I often end up doing something I do not really want to do for fear that if I do not, people will criticize me in my absence.
5. When someone says they want a meeting with me next week but do not say what it is about, I spend a lot of time worrying that I have done something wrong.
6. I often find myself offering to do things for people out of guilt rather than a genuine desire to help them.
7. I am easily unsettled if my parents-in-law do not agree with the way I discipline my child(ren).
8. I am afraid to discipline my child(ren) for fear that they will not love me any more.
9. I feel guilty when I cannot comply with what my mother or father is asking of me.
10. I pay more attention to the criticism of one person than to the praise and admiration of the other 99.
11. I constantly look for affirmation from those closest to me.
12. I often find myself quickly apologizing in order to make peace, even though I do not feel I am to blame.

For an analysis of total scores see Notes at end of book (p. 89).

Taking it further

1. Look for opportunities to explain the reason 'why' when children ask questions about everyday activities.
2. Try to be aware of your own responses to situations and ask yourself why you do what you do.
3. Read Chapter 6 of *Family Time*.

Recommended reading for this session

J John, *Ten*, Kingsway Publications, 2000

7

Training and Obedience

This is a subject that arouses many different emotions and opinions. It is unfortunate that the word 'discipline' has lost its proper meaning today. It has come to imply punishment or smacking. Real discipline is much more than this. Its focus is on reaching and training the heart.

Wise words from God's word

Proverbs 23:19 says, 'Listen, my son, and be wise, and keep your heart on the right path.' We read in Luke 6:45, 'The good man brings good things out of the good stored up in his heart.' And Proverbs 22:15a says, 'Folly is bound up in the heart of a child.'

Children naturally sometimes do silly and unwise things. The job of Mum and Dad is to give instruction to our children so as to encourage them to have hearts that are wise. This is the purpose of discipline, and when looked at in this broader context it becomes an area of exciting opportunity rather than one of tension and stress.

Proverbs 22:6 says, 'Train a child in the way he should go, and when he is old he will not turn from it.' And Proverbs 1:7b-9 tells us, 'Fools despise wisdom and discipline. Listen, my son, to your father's instruction and do not forsake your mother's teaching. They will be a garland to grace your head and a chain to adorn your neck.'

Obedience is probably not the most fashionable concept these days, but when it is evident it is a very attractive thing, and it brings real peace and harmony to the family. Our aim as parents can be obedience on the part of our children. The Bible encourages this in many different places, and it does so for the good of our children. Colossians 3:20, for example, says, 'Children, obey your parents in everything, for this pleases the Lord.' God's intention in giving us our children was that we should give them instruction and correction as well as care and nurture.

Spend a few moments talking with your partner or neighbour about your immediate response to the question of obedience.

Sometimes parents take on the role of adviser rather than parent. Often we have little confidence that our children will do as we ask. We therefore see children making decisions and parents suggesting options. Sometimes our children have too much choice.

Let's acknowledge our responsibility. Let's see ourselves not as care providers but as parents, with a responsibility to care for, nurture, correct and instruct our children. There are many benefits for our children in this.

- To live in obedience to parents brings *safety* for our children. In Ephesians 6:1–3, God has drawn a circle of great blessing. It says, 'Children, obey your parents in the Lord, for this is right. "Honour your father and mother" – which is the first commandment with a promise – "that it may go well with you and that you may enjoy long life on the earth".' If children live within that circle of obedience to their parents, things will go well. It is a place of safety.

- It will help them in their own *relationship with God*. It will be through obedience to God that they will learn to hear his voice and respond to him.
- Children who have been taught and encouraged in obedience will respond well to *authority* in general (e.g. at work later in life) and will thus grow in wisdom and understanding (see Proverbs 15:5; 29:15).

It is good to respect authority and to teach our children to do the same.

Authority is needed for *order*. If it were not for authority, we would risk our lives every time we went out in the car, we would have no certainty that our savings were safe in the hands of the bank or building society, and buying food from the supermarket would become a health hazard.

Authority also helps us to be *considerate* and to think of others. If we all just do our own thing, others suffer – including ourselves in the end.

It is good not only to teach our children to obey the rules, but also to talk to them about why we obey them.

Our children tend to copy us – they pick up our attitudes. If they see us disregarding authority, they are likely to do the same. If, on the other hand, we respect authority, our children will probably follow us in that.

Here are a couple of warnings:

- Like our children, we too can fall short (and often do). We may need to say 'sorry' to our children, for example, if we find ourselves exploding at them.
- Remember what Colossians 3:21 says: 'Fathers, do not embitter your children, or they will become discouraged.' We need to be thoughtful and try to avoid unnecessary exasperation.

Obedience in practice

There will be times when our children will ignore or oppose our reasonable instructions. What can we do? We can teach them how to respond. So often our children are willing to respond if we will only show them how.

When we ask our children to do something such as tidy their room or help to wash up, we can reasonably expect a response such as 'Yes, Mum' or 'Yes, Dad', followed by a willingness to carry out what we have requested. After all, most children will respond immediately to the request, 'Please would you get ready – I want to take you to McDonald's', and so can surely respond just as quickly to other requests. If we allow our children continually to get away with not doing as they are asked, we will in effect teach them to be disobedient. We will teach them that obedience is not a priority.

Children often respond to their parents' resolve and nothing more. So often it is we, the parents, who unwittingly teach disobedience, while desiring obedience. Below are some of the ways in which parents might undermine their own efforts – and we all fall into these traps from time to time!

1. We threaten and repeat ourselves
2. We use bribes
3. We negotiate in the midst of conflict
4. We misuse compassion
5. We offer too much choice

If we allow our children constantly to make their own choices, it is difficult for them to give up that choice when the crunch comes. How do we know when our children are ready to have choices? They are ready to have choices when they can live happily without them!

Ten tips for addressing our children

1. Say what you mean and mean what you say.
2. Be careful how you phrase your instruction.
3. Get eye contact and a verbal response.
4. Don't be too quick to repeat yourself.
5. Expect a response.
6. Provide a warning.
7. Offer a door of escape.
8. Consider the setting.
9. Be consistent.
10. Remember your example.

Conflict is inevitable in every family, and it is helpful to view it not as a negative thing, but as an opportunity to move our children forward in the right direction.

- For our *younger children* (up to four years old), conflict can give us the opportunity – if we deal with it in a positive way – to establish in their minds that they need to learn to obey Mum and Dad.
- For our *older children*, we can use rebellious or inappropriate behaviour as an opportunity to help them understand that what they are doing is an indication of what is going on in their hearts, and that what will help is a change of heart.

A good safety valve

Our children have thoughts and ideas of their own which need to be heard. Once they have grasped the need for obedience (probably around the age of five), it is a good idea to teach our children that it is fine to ask us to think again about what we have asked them to do, as long as it is done respectfully. This is a good thing because:

- We may have spoken in a hurry without thinking about what we were saying. It allows us to change our mind about something which in retrospect is inappropriate.
- It protects our children from feeling that they are always in a no-win situation. It is a good safety valve for them to know that Mum and Dad will listen to them and reconsider an instruction if necessary and appropriate.

You could encourage your children to respond like this:

1. On hearing us call they begin to act straight away.
2. They ask us to rethink respectfully, and not in a whine.
3. They accept graciously that Mum and Dad have the final word.

We as parents can also think ahead, weigh up what we are about to instruct, and check for ourselves whether it is necessary and appropriate.

Setting boundaries for very young children

The earlier we start this obedience training the better – in fact, we should start it as soon as a child begins deliberately to disregard our instructions.

**Set limits and boundaries right from the start.
Do not give your baby freedoms which
you may later regret.**

The purpose of setting boundaries for our children is not to take away their freedom to explore, but to give them freedom within manageable limits, according to how much they can understand.

1. Use a playpen

If you start from when your baby is very young (say four weeks), but old enough to lie under a baby gym, he will get used to it right from the beginning. He will be able to focus more easily on his toys without the distraction of lots of space around him, and will likely feel safe within his physical boundaries. Also, if you build playpen times into your baby's routine, you will find yourself with periods in the day when you can get on with chores in the knowledge that your baby is safe and happy in the playpen.

2. Do not be afraid to say 'no' to your baby

'No' simply defines the necessary boundaries. The key to setting limits for your little one is not in controlling his environment by removing everything, but by training him to your voice.

3. Learn how to deal with tantrums

Sometimes our young children, on hearing the word 'no', will throw a tantrum. The way in which we, as parents, deal with tantrums will have a bearing on whether they become frequent. If the tantrum is successful – in other words, if it enables the child to get what he wants – the behaviour may reoccur. If, on the other hand, it does not achieve the desired result the first time, it is less likely to be repeated.

What can we do when a tantrum occurs? If it is a tantrum born out of frustration, because the child cannot physically manage to make the Lego model he has in his mind's eye, then we can be sympathetic and help out if required. However, if it is clearly a temper tantrum, it is good to remove the child to a cot or, if you are in public, to strap him into a buggy away from people until he has calmed down. For a child of more than about two and a half, it is good for him to know that once he has calmed down there will be a consequence to his tantrum. This will help him not to repeat it in the future.

Our aim is not to focus on behaviour, but rather to see behaviour as an indication of what is going on in our children's hearts.

**A willingness to be obedient demonstrates
a heart that wants to do the right thing.**

Taking it further

1. Spend some time working on obedience, putting into practice some of the suggestions from this session.
2. If you have younger children, try making a game out of your child coming the first time he is called with a 'Yes, Mum' or a 'Yes, Dad.'
3. Try giving a five-minute warning before giving instructions and see how it makes a difference to your child's response.
4. Read Chapter 7 of *Family Time*.

8

Taking Corrective Action

Our focus here is not so much on correction, but rather on our children's hearts. A number of different approaches can be adopted which will be positive and encouraging as well as corrective.

Our children will need the positive and encouraging as well as the corrective if we are to reach their hearts and not frustrate them.

It is worth reminding ourselves of the importance of parenting with the long-term aim in mind. We are not just disciplining for the moment, nor are we just responding to a situation in order to resolve a crisis. Instead we are looking to be consistent in what we do, in order to reach our children's hearts. Here are some questions to consider.

- Where are our children's hearts?
- What is their motive for doing what they are doing?
- Have we given them proper instruction?
- Do they know what they are meant to be doing and why?

We can all train our children to behave like machines by punishing them when they misbehave. This is not our aim. Our aim is to use discipline as a whole, in order to reach the point where our children know what is right and desire to do it because it is the right thing. Remember, however, that the whole thing is a process and we will not always get it right. The important thing is to think ahead and have a plan.

Let's start our exploration of the different areas of discipline by distinguishing between abilities and behaviour.

Abilities

Abilities are not behavioural issues and so do not have a corrective side to them. They are achievements – such as riding a bike or learning to swim – that need discipline if the skills are to be acquired successfully. We can encourage our child to learn an ability through offering two things:

- Praise
- Incentives

Behaviour

Behaviour is an indication of what is going on inside our child's heart. It is motivated by two things:

- Encouragement
- Correction

Encouragement

There is so much we can do to encourage our children in their behaviour. We can encourage them to behave well. With forethought we can encourage them by giving them prior preparation so that they have every opportunity to do the right thing. So often children want to do the right thing, but often miss out because they have not been encouraged to do so.

On the way to spend the day with friends, for example, we might ask our children, 'What are the "Golden Rules" when we're at a friend's house?' They will have great fun seeing how many things they can think of:

- Say 'hello' when we arrive.
- Take shoes off at the door.
- Say 'please' and 'thank you'.
- Do not charge around the house.
- Ask before playing with toys.
- Look at adults when you speak to them.

As well as reminding them of the 'Golden Rules', such an exercise also helps them to own what they have said – and this encourages them to carry out what they have spoken about. Then we can have the joy of praising them for remembering all the 'Golden Rules', and afterwards we can praise them again for doing so well while we were at our friend's house.

Correction

Sometimes encouragement is not always enough, and our children get it wrong and find themselves in trouble. Then comes the need for correction.

Wise words from God's word

'No discipline seems pleasant at the time, but painful. Later on, however, it produces a harvest of righteousness and peace for those who have been trained by it' (Hebrews 12:11). Correction is clearly an integral part of discipline.

Loving parents seek to discipline their children wisely and thoughtfully.

Remember another important verse from the Bible: 'Let your gentleness be evident to all' (Philippians 4:5). If we can approach correction with this in mind, we cannot go far wrong.

It is good to consider the *motivation* behind a child's particular action or behaviour before we consider taking any corrective action ourselves. Was it accidental or intentional? Was it done out of:

1. childish innocence?
2. childish thoughtlessness?
3. deliberate naughtiness?

The way in which we answer this question will determine the form of correction we use.

1. Childish innocence

When our children behave badly, it is not always deliberate. Sometimes it is simply a result of childish innocence. It may be that they do not realize, because they have never been told, that what they have done is wrong.

2. Childish thoughtlessness

Sometimes what our children do is not rebellious but thoughtless. We will need great sensitivity and wisdom as we seek to correct our children's childish behaviour. Sometimes we will simply need to give them proper instruction so that it does not happen again. At other times a light telling-off may be required and may be a consequence to help them remember.

3. Deliberate naughtiness

At times children are deliberately naughty.

- They might kick a football inside the house where windows can get broken.
- They might answer back.

- They might refuse to be corrected, or refuse to comply with what we have asked them to do.
- They might be indirectly defiant by pretending not to hear, pleading ignorance, sulking or whining.

We all know our own children, and it is good to respond to deliberate naughtiness according to their general character and age. We can ask ourselves these questions:

- Have the circumstances not helped my child to be obedient?
- Is he particularly tired, or hungry?
- Is he acting out of character, or is this something that often occurs and really needs to be dealt with?
- Is he unwell, or is he sickening for something?

Let's be careful when giving correction that we do not overdo it. Correction that is heavier than the crime is very disheartening for our children.

Generally, deliberate naughtiness will fall into the following types – although this is only a guide and things are rarely so black and white.

a) Small incidents that need a telling-off

Sometimes our children will do something which they should know is naughty, or which they were corrected for three months ago, but perhaps they have genuinely forgotten or had a momentary lapse. They may know that they have to put their bikes away in the garden shed at the end of the day, for example, but have omitted to do it on this occasion. For something like this we would just give a warning and some encouragement not to forget next time.

b) Naughtiness that needs more than just a verbal telling-off

Correction might be needed for behaviour that occurs frequently, for warnings that have not been heeded, or for past habits that seem to be growing more regular again. In these cases a stronger telling-off might be appropriate, accompanied by an enforced temporary break from whatever activity the children are involved in, in order to give them some thinking time to consider what they were doing wrong and hopefully to have a 'change of heart'. Sometimes a permanent break from the activity for that day might help them to remember not to repeat whatever they were doing wrong.

In terms of undesirable habits, *whining* is something that will quickly become a habit if it is left to develop. How can we cope with whining? Can we stop it in a positive way?

- As a first step, point out that this whining is becoming a habit and that it is not an acceptable means of communicating. This in itself may have a good impact. Often we get into habits without being aware of it, and children are just the same.
- For a toddler it is often helpful just to say, 'No whining,' and have them answer you, 'Yes, Mum/Dad. No whining.' It is amazing how effective this can be, simply because, having spoken those words, they have owned the fact that whining is not acceptable.
- For a slightly older child, if requests come in a whine, you might suggest that your child goes away and has a rethink, then comes back and asks properly.
- If whining still persists, a stronger form of correction may be needed.

c) Behaviour that will need stronger action

There are various options for stronger forms of correction.

Time apart from others can work very well. Children are very social beings and love being with other children and adults. To be separated from other people in a cot or bedroom, or even to sit on the stairs away from the centre of activity, removes that privilege and for many is a very effective means of correction.

Smacking is another option, but one fraught with difficulty. It is often approached so aggressively that it is tantamount to physical abuse. We are all aware that the smacking of children by parents has been challenged recently through the courts, and the government has backed parents to use 'reasonable chastisement' when disciplining their own children. It is understandable that the practice of smacking has been questioned, but we should also remember that when a parent rants and raves uncontrollably at their child it is just as violent and abusive as an out-of-control slap. The problem with out-of-control smacking is that the emotional pain caused by arbitrary, thoughtless 'discipline' is made worse by the physical abuse.

Any punishment given to a child in an unthought-out, careless or vengeful fashion is abusive.

Smacking is not an alternative to reaching our children's hearts by teaching them to show love and self-control and to do the right thing. In fact, unless we are actively working at building loving relationships and a strong, secure home, as well as encouraging and teaching good values to our children, smacking (and any other unthought-out punishment) is really not an option. Smacking alone will not result in a changed heart.

Individual parents will need to make up their own minds about whether it is right to smack their child. If we do decide it is an option, what is important is *how* the smack is given. Here are a few practical guidelines.

- Smacking should be reserved for wilful defiance.
- Smacking should be administered with consistency, and not just on the days when we are short of patience. Children are born gamblers: if they are expecting a smack and do not get one, they will try it again.
- Smacking should be done in private to maintain the child's dignity, and only ever by the parent.

- Smacking should only ever sting, never cause physical injury.
- Most importantly, smacking should be done in a loving atmosphere, not in anger by an out-of-control parent, and the child should understand fully why he is having the smack. The child needs to be reassured of the parent's love before *and* after, and once things have calmed down he needs to know that is the end of it.

The withdrawal of a privilege is another corrective option. This might include removal of pocket money or treats, not being allowed to stay up late at the weekend, not being allowed to use a favourite toy for a set period, not being allowed to watch a favourite TV programme, and so on. We all know what is appropriate for our own child.

Setting up logical consequences is an idea that ties in closely with withdrawal of a privilege, but the consequence would be something directly related to the behaviour in question. As our children get older, they will often respond more readily to logical consequences.

We will need much wisdom as we decide which form of correction to use. Do not be afraid to take time to think and pray before you act. The right course of action is not always clear cut. It is important, however, to stress the need for some correction, whatever form it might take. If we seek to avoid it entirely, we will probably become very frustrated with our disobedient children. Training our children will involve both encouragement *and* correction.

The most important thing to remember is that our children need to know that we love them unconditionally. If our children believe we love them, they will respond so much more readily to our discipline, be it encouragement or correction.

Putting things right

It is a good thing for our children to learn the importance not just of receiving correction for their disobedience, but also of feeling repentant, of having a change of heart or attitude which will result in an outward change of behaviour.

Feeling repentant

It is very easy to feel regret without feeling repentant. To be truly repentant has an important effect in the restoration of a relationship. Just as in the Christian life we continually repent of the things which spoil our relationship with God, so it is with our relationships within the family. We can teach our children how their disobedient and selfish acts can spoil their family relationships.

Forgiving and forgetting

**To say 'sorry' only goes part of the way:
it acknowledges a mistake.
To ask for forgiveness demonstrates
a change of heart.**

You might help your children to appreciate this powerful distinction by encouraging them to say, 'I'm sorry – will you forgive me?' when they have been disobedient or when they have fallen out with a brother or sister.

Mum and Dad can say 'sorry' too

Forgiveness works both ways, and if we are in the wrong it will be very powerful for our children to hear us say 'sorry' and to ask for forgiveness.

Making amends

Sometimes we are faced with a question of personal responsibility. Saying 'I'm sorry' and asking for forgiveness is not enough if you have created a financial liability, whether accidentally or intentionally. It may be necessary to make amends in a tangible way if something tangible has been damaged.

Taking it further

1. Spend some time thinking and talking about how you feel about the way you discipline your children, and discuss any changes that you want to make.
2. Find an opportunity to encourage your children in learning an ability.
3. Start putting into practice the encouragement that will help your children know how to respond on different occasions. Try, for example, giving them instruction on what is expected of them at the supermarket or at a friend's house.
4. Look out for examples of 'childish innocence' and 'deliberate naughtiness'. Is it easy to spot the difference?
5. Read Chapter 8 of *Family Time*.

9

Modelling Love and Respect

Teaching our children to value and respect other people

Children often find doing the right thing much easier than adults do. Where they often fall down is in not knowing what to do in the first place.

'People matter' is a great family value to hold, but it is meaningless unless our children know and understand how it is worked out in practice.

1. Our children's relationship with God

In order to love God, our children will need to learn, in childlike ways, to do the things that we do as adults.

- It will mean *becoming familiar with the Bible.*
- It will mean *learning to pray.*
- It will mean *taking them to church.*
- It will mean *learning to value all that God has made.*
- It will mean *reminding our children constantly that all the gifts they have come from God.*

Finally, here are some ideas about what you – as a family – might do to show that you value others, especially those less fortunate than yourselves.

- Sponsor a child in a developing country, for example through the Toybox Charity.[1]
- Raise money for a project that helps the homeless.
- Give clothes and toys to others more needy than your own family.
- At Christmas take part in a project that gives toys to children who otherwise would not have any, for example through the Samaritans Purse Organization.[2]

Many of the things we have mentioned here will not come naturally! We will need to work at it, but it is our firm belief that, as we gently and prayerfully teach and encourage our children to love God, it will gradually become a way of life for them.

2. Our children's relationship with Mum and Dad

What can we do to help our children to respect Mum and Dad?

We should be wary of trying to be friends with our children from day one. To be a parent is a privilege, so let's be just that. To seek to be friends confuses our children and implies an equal relationship, which is not possible when you consider all the responsibility that we have as parents.

Friendship is our ultimate goal in adulthood, and we reach it gradually.

We can also help our children to respect us by *teaching them to be careful how they speak to us and by correcting them if they are rude.* Just because we adults recognize rudeness does not mean that our children will, however, so we should take care to point it out gently.

Here are some ideas for practical things we can do to encourage our children to respect us.

- Have Mum and Dad sit at the head of the table at family mealtimes.

- Have Mum and Dad sit in the front seats of the car.
- Have younger children ask before taking a drink or a biscuit and before using the telephone.

3. Our children's relationship with their brothers and sisters

What can we do to help our children value their brothers and sisters, and to demonstrate that people matter in this very special family relationship?

- Try referring to your children's siblings as 'your brother' or 'your sister' as a change from calling them by their Christian name. This is a good way of reinforcing the relationship for them and helping them to know what a special thing it is. Also you could say things like, 'Isn't it lovely that N is your brother/sister?' This serves to *remind them that a brother or sister is great to have* – someone with whom they will always be the best of friends and therefore need to take care of.
- *When one of them is being kind to the other, try to praise them for it.* This brings to their attention the fact that what they did was to think of others rather than themselves, and it will encourage them, having received praise for it, to do it again next time.
- Try to *encourage them to be glad when something good happens to one of their siblings,* and praise them when they manage it.
- Squabbles between brothers and sisters are inevitable, but they need not get out of hand. It is sad to hear brothers and sisters calling each other names or putting each other down. There is a proverb that says, 'Reckless words pierce like a sword, but the tongue of the wise brings healing' (Proverbs 12:18). We should not underestimate the harm that can be done if a child is constantly put down by a sibling. Equally, we should not underestimate the good that can come from the carefully chosen words of a loving brother or sister. *Encourage your children to be sensitive to one another's feelings.* Teach them how to listen and

respond to one another in a way that will build each other up.

- *Encourage your children to be aware of the good qualities that their brothers and sisters have.* Periodically during family time, ask the children what they especially like about each of the others. This not only reinforces in our children positive feelings towards their siblings, but also encourages each of them as they learn of qualities they perhaps did not know they had.

4. Our children's relationship with other adults

What can we do to help our children demonstrate respect for other adults?

- *Devise some family guidelines for your children about what to do when an adult speaks to them.* Shyness is very common among young children, but they will feel much more confident if they have prior preparation about what to do and say.
- *Teach your children how to get your attention in an appropriate way* when you are in conversation with another adult.
- *Encourage your children from an early age to write thank-you letters for the presents they receive,* as a means of demonstrating an awareness of the preciousness of others.
- *When you go to a public place* such as a library or doctor's surgery, or to certain church services where people particularly need peace and quiet, you could remind the children of that before you arrive.
- *Mealtimes are always a great opportunity for thinking of others.* Encourage your children to use good manners by not starting until everyone is served, by saying 'please' and 'thank you', by eating with their mouths closed, and by complimenting the cook. Even babies can use good manners. You could teach your baby sign language so that he can say 'please' and 'thank you' and 'more, please' and 'drink, please' before they can speak (babies can often pick this up from about a year, sometimes earlier).

5. Our children's relationship with their friends

What can we do, in this age of competition, to encourage our children to value their friends and peers?

- *We can help them to be glad when something good happens to one of their friends.*
- *Encourage them to respect their friends' belongings* and, at other people's houses, to wait until they are invited to play with the toys, or at least to ask before they dive in.
- *Encourage them to look out for children who might be on their own* in the playground and to include them in their games.
- To the moan of 'It's not fair', *explain to the children that life is not always fair*, and help them to remember and be thankful for what they have rather than what they do not have.
- *Encourage them to pray for their friends* – not just generally, but for specific needs.
- *Encourage them to feel very privileged when they receive an invitation to a party.* Remind them what a privilege it is to be counted as someone's friend.

Here are some ideas about how you can reinforce the idea of a party invitation from a friend being something special.

- Encourage them to make their own wrapping paper by colouring blank sheets of paper.
- Encourage them to make their own birthday card to give to their friend.
- Let them choose and wrap the present with you.
- Have them pay a bit towards the present when they are old enough.

In the early years, our children learn more from copying what we do than we realize.

Taking it further

1. Spot your child being kind to a sibling or friend without being prompted, and give him or her lots of praise.
2. Teach your children how to get your attention when you are talking to another person, and see how long it takes for them to catch on.
3. Read Chapter 9 of *Family Time*.

10

Keeping the Vision in Mind

The Bible talks in several places of the triad of faith, hope and love, three key qualities in our Christian walk. These three qualities are just as key in holding on to our dreams and visions for our families.

Faith

God is faithful, and we can trust him to take care of every aspect of our family life if we entrust it to him. He will honour those families who seek to honour him. As we prayerfully commit our ways to him, he will watch over us and guide us in our family life.

Have faith that with God's help you can build a better marriage. Here are some actions you might take to help you invest in your marriage.

- Take time for each other.
- Look for the good and the beautiful in each other.
- Stand together with a mutual sense of values and a common objective.
- Speak words of appreciation.
- Find things to praise in each other.
- Always have the capacity to forgive and forget.
- Do not be a historical partner – one who always digs up the past – because you can bury a marriage with a lot of little digs.

- Look to the future, think how you would like it to be, and then go for it.

It is not just about marrying the right partner, but about *being* the right partner.

We will also be strengthened as parents if we can maintain faith in the following things:

- Have faith to believe that you are God's appointed parents for your children.
- Have faith in your values.
- Have faith in your methods of discipline.
- Have faith that God has heard your prayers for your children.

Hope

Hope is a great thing. It allows us to stand firm. Hope is an integral part of being a parent. As parents we *need* hope.

- We hope that our children have caught our values.
- We hope that they will find a mission in life.
- We hope that when our children are small we have instilled in them a sense of purpose, a thirst to make the best of all things, and a desire to make a difference in this world.

The question 'What do you want to do when you grow up?' is so much more rewarding when it concerns not just economic activities but values, character and the contribution that your child hopes to make to the future shape of this world.

Love

Our children need to know our unconditional love – a love that is accepting yet guiding.

What we are seeking to provide at home is *a place of security and love* – a place where our children know they will always be loved and looked after; a place where they can just be who God has called them to be; a place where they are allowed to fail as well as succeed. This is the value that holds this course together: the value of love.

- Love does not demand performance and always forgives.
- Love should seek to build up and guide in right ways.
- Love should not be afraid to discipline for a better end.
- Love will commit you to start praying for your family.
- Love will commit you to make time to be with your children.

Creating a family vision statement

A family vision statement will give you a fixed point of reference. You can look at it from time to time and ask yourselves the following questions.

- How are we doing as a family?
- Are we living out the things we consider to be important?
- Are we spending time together?
- How are we treating each other?
- Are we being encouraging?
- Are we giving as well as taking?
- Are we thinking of those outside the family as well as ourselves?
- Is our home a place of peace and harmony, a place to which we all enjoy coming back?
- Are we living as God would have us live?

Step 1

Either at family time or round the family meal table, introduce the idea of having a family vision statement. Explain what it is and see what people think of the idea. Do not push it! If there is little interest, leave it until another time. Unless everyone owns it, they will not be committed to it. If they seem excited by the idea, go on to Step 2.

Step 2

Explain that at the next family time, or some other appointed time, you can all start to put the vision statement together. You might suggest that it could include the following things:

- What kind of family do we want to be?
- What kind of atmosphere do we want in our home?
- How do we want to treat each other and speak to one another?
- What are the responsibilities of each family member?
- What things are important to us as a family?
- What guidelines do we want to live by?
- How do we want to treat other people?
- What is the purpose of our family?
- How can we make a difference to the community in which we live?

Make it clear that each member will have an opportunity to say what they think is important. Encourage each family member to go off and think carefully about what they want to be included in the family vision statement.

Step 3

At the appointed time, come back together with a piece of paper and begin to discuss your vision statement. Go round the family and take turns to say the things you feel are important. Discuss them as you go, and write them down. You will need some ground rules:

- Everyone listens when someone is speaking.
- Everyone respects what others say.
- Everyone has a chance to say everything they want to say.

Step 4

Once you have a draft, leave it for a while so that people can think about it, revisit it, and agree changes if necessary.

Step 5

Once everyone is happy with the vision statement, create the final document, have everyone sign it and date it, and then display it in the place where you most often gather as a family. Use it to keep your destination in mind.

Step 6

Review your vision statement every year.

Below, to give you some ideas, is an example of a vision statement created by one family who followed the Family Time course (reproduced with their permission).

> **Things that are important to our family**
> 1. All of us are to tell the truth.
> 2. First time obedience to Mum and Dad.
> 3. Mum and Dad not to aggravate the children.
> 4. Stealing is always wrong. When we borrow things – we will look after them as if they were our own and not be jealous.
> 5. We will support and encourage each other, especially when we get things wrong.
> 6. We will listen to each other.
> 7. We will show kindness to each other by sharing our own things and time e.g. by helping around the house.
> 8. Remember: people are more important than things.
> 9. It's important to have fun and laughter together as a family.
> 10. We love God and want to serve him.

Take time now to discuss with your partner or neighbour some of the things that you would want to put into your family vision statement. Write down the three things that are most important to you. Think about how you might go about creating your family vision statement.

Notes

Chapter 1

1. Steven Covey, *The Seven Habits of Highly Effective Families* (Simon & Schuster Ltd, 1998).

Chapter 3

1. Ted Tripp, *Shepherding a Child's Heart* (Shepherd Press, 1995).

Chapter 6

The second part of this session is based on ideas from *Growing Kids God's Way* by Gary and Anne-Marie Ezzo.

Total scores
91–120   Excessively unhealthy conscience
73–90   Fairly unhealthy conscience
54–72   Moderately unhealthy conscience
41–53   Slightly unhealthy conscience
29–40   Healthy conscience
12–28   Possibly a hardened conscience!

Chapter 9

1. The Toybox Charity (Helping Street Children in Guatemala) is

contactable at: PO Box 660, Amersham, Bucks HP6 6EA; e-mail: *info@toybox.org*; website: *www.toybox.org*.

2. The Samaritans Purse Organization (working with children in the Eastern Bloc) is contactable at: Samaritans Purse Int. Ltd, Victoria House, Victoria Road, Buckhurst Hill, Essex IG9 5EX; e-mail: *info@samaritans-purse.org.uk*.

PERSONAL NOTES

PERSONAL NOTES

PERSONAL NOTES

PERSONAL NOTES